www.oxfordowl.co.uk

G000020469

Well done!

Busy worker!

Smart work!

Good work!

Busy worker!

Well done!

Well done!

Smart work!

Busy worker!

Good work!

WARNING!
NOT SUITABLE FOR
CHILDREN UNDER
36 MONTHS DUE
TO SMALL PARTS
WHICH PRESENT A
CHOKING HAZARD.

Sarah Lindsay

At Home With MENTAL MATHS

OXFORD

UNIVERSITY PRESS

Introduction

The *At Home With* workbooks introduce and reinforce key numeracy and literacy concepts for primary school children. They provide lots of opportunities to develop the key skills that are the basis of primary school curriculum work. The workbooks are available in three levels: 3–5 years, 5–7 years, and 7–9 years. The activities are fun and are designed to stimulate discussion, as well as practical skills. Some children will be able to complete the activities alone, after initial discussion; others may benefit from adult support throughout. All children will enjoy rewarding themselves with a sticker when they reach the end of an activity.

Using the book

- Your child will be doing some mathematics every day in school. Working through the activities in this book will ensure that your child has the best possible support during these early years.
  The activities will:
  - help your child achieve the all-important learning targets for children aged 7 to 9.
  - be fun to work on so that your child will enjoy mathematics.
- Each double page spread is devoted to a separate topic, and each page is divided into three stages: **Warm up** (revises previous knowledge), **Learn about** (teaches a particular concept), and **Now try these** (gives a practical application). These give your child a natural progression through each topic.

Helping your child

- Always talk through the work on the page to make sure your child understands what he or she is working on.
- Don't do too much in one sitting. One double page spread is probably enough at a time for a child's concentration span.
- Most importantly, give plenty of praise and encouragement. Learning always works best when based on success, fun, and enjoyment!

OXFORD
UNIVERSITY PRESS

Great Clarendon Street, Oxford OX2 6DP

Oxford University Press is a department of the University of Oxford.
Oxford is a registered trade mark of Oxford University Press
in the UK and in certain other countries

© Oxford University Press 2009

Author Sarah Lindsay
Cover illustration by Charlie Fowkes
Inside illustrations by Bill Bolton

Database right Oxford University Press (maker)

First published in 2009
This edition 2013

All rights reserved.

You must not circulate this book in any other binding or cover
and you must impose this same condition on any acquirer

British Library Cataloguing in Publication Data

Data available

ISBN: 978-0-19-274468-5
2 4 6 8 10 9 7 5 3

Printed in India by Manipal Technologies Ltd

Paper used in the production of this book is a natural,
recyclable product made from wood grown in sustainable forests.
The manufacturing process conforms to the environmental
regulations of the country of origin.

CONTENTS

Numbers to 20

▼ Warm up

a) 4 + 7 = 11   b) 11 + 8 = 19   c) 12 + 2 = 14   d) 10 + 7 = 17

e) 9 + 5 = 14   f) 12 + 6 = 18   g) 14 + 3 = 7   h) 15 + 4 = 19

▼ Learn about

It is useful to know your number bonds to 20.
Fill in the gaps so each number sentence totals 20.

a) 12 + 8 = 20   b) 4 + 16 = 20   c) 17 + 3 = 20   d) 7 + 13 = 20

e) 15 + 5 = 20   f) 2 + 18 = 20

▼ Now try these

1. In each group, circle the two numbers that total 20.

a) 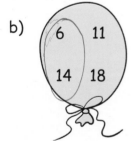   b)   c) 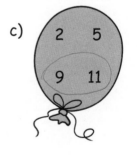   d)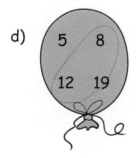

4   7
12   13

6   11
14   18

2   5
9   11

5   8
12   19

2. Jake had saved £9 and for his birthday he
was given £11. How much money did Jake now have?   £ 20

3. Balloons were tied all around the house
to celebrate Jake's birthday. There were
7 outside, 6 in the living room and 7 in the kitchen.
How many balloons were there altogether?   20 balloons

Numbers to 20

▼ Warm up

a) 9 − 6 = 6

b) 12 − 4 = 9

c) 16 − 8 = ...

d) 10 − 3 = ...

e) 7 − 4 = 3

f) 18 − 5 = 13

g) 17 − 8 = ...

h) 11 − 9 = ...

▼ Learn about

When you subtract, there is a way to check that you have the right answer. Add your answer to what was taken away – it should equal the starting number.

the answer   the starting number

$$20 - 7 = 13 \quad \text{so} \quad 13 + 7 = 20$$

the number subtracted

Mark these number sentences with a ✓ or a ✗.

a) 20 − 6 = 14 ....

b) 5 − 11 = 3 ....

c) 19 − 11 = 8 ....

▼ Now try these

1. Fill the gaps in these number sentences.
Check you have answered them correctly.

a) 19 − .... = 2

b) 12 − 9 = ...

c) 20 − .... = 20

d) .... − 7 = 13

e) .... − 7 = 6

f) 12 − 5 = ...

2. Jake invited 16 friends to his birthday party.
Liam, Jay and Meena couldn't come.
How many of Jake's friends came to the party? ....

3. One game played at Jake's party
was called 'Hunt the sweets!'
20 packets of sweets were hidden but only 13 were
found. How many more packets were there to find? ....

Addition

▼ Warm up

a) £1 + 50p + 2p = ...

b) 50p + 20p = ...

c) £1 + 5p + 5p = ...

d) £1 + 50p + 10p = ...

e) £1 + 20p + 20p = ...

f) £2 + 50p + 50p = ...

▼ Learn about

Numbers can be added in any order.

start with the units

23 + 46 = 69 = 46 + 23 = 69

Remember to add units and tens separately
when adding big numbers together.

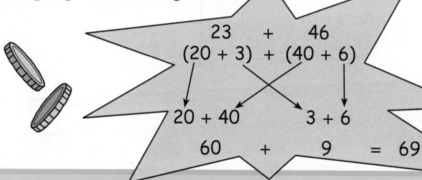

23 + 46
(20 + 3) + (40 + 6)

20 + 40   3 + 6

60 + 9 = 69

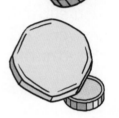

▼ Now try these

1. Add together the numbers on the counters.
The first one has been done for you.

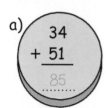

a)
34
+ 51
—
85
....

b)
20
+ 29
—
....

c)
31
+ 36
—
....

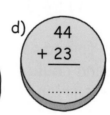

d)
44
+ 23
—
....

e)
62
+ 37
—
....

2. Choose 2 numbers between 10 and 50. Write them here ....
Now add the numbers together! ....

6

Addition

▼ Warm up

Add these consecutive numbers.

a)
| 22 | 23 |
45

b)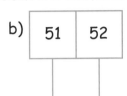
| 51 | 52 |

c)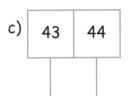
| 43 | 44 |

d)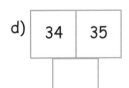
| 34 | 35 |

e)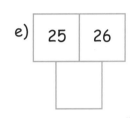
| 25 | 26 |

▼ Learn about

When answering addition problems, it always helps to know the different ways addition problems can be worded.

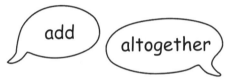 add · altogether · what is the sum of? · plus · find the total

Answer these questions.

a) Find the sum of 14, 12 and 10. ....

b) How many altogether are 8, 14 and 22? ....

c) What is 34 plus 55? ....

d) Find the total of 26 and 19. ....

▼ Now try these

1. Nila was skipping.
First she scored 37.
Next she scored 34.
How many did she score altogether? ....

2. Daisy skipped next. She scored 15.
What is the sum of all the scores? ....

7

Subtraction

▼ **Warm up**   Take away each of these numbers from 46.
The first one has been done for you.

a)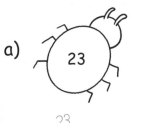
23
.....23.....

b)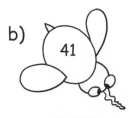
41
....

c)
35
....

d)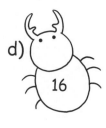
16
....

e)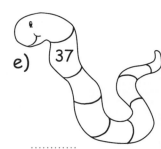
37
....

▼ **Learn about**   Numbers cannot be subtracted in any order.

Remember you can check a subtraction problem with an addition. Look back at page 5 if you need reminding.

| 48 − 23 cannot be changed to 23 − 48 |

▼ **Now try these**   1. Using only the following numbers, write as many subtraction number sentences as you can.
One has been done for you.

| 32 | 17 | 56 | 7 | 39 | 49 |

a) .... − .... = ...

b) ..56.. − ..17.. = ...39..

c) .... − .... = ...

d) .... − .... = ...

e) .... − .... = ...

2. Four snails had a race. Snail A travelled 18cm. Snail B travelled 9cm.
Snail C travelled 23cm. Snail D travelled 36cm.

a) How much further did Snail A travel than Snail B? ....

b) How much further did Snail C travel than Snail B? ....

c) How much further did the winning snail travel than Snail A? ....

8

Subtraction

▼ Warm up

Fill in the gaps.

a) 34 − 15 = ...

b) 42 − .... = 20

c) .... − 12 = 37

d) 47 − 28 = ...

e) 28 − .... = 9

f) .... − 21 = 48

▼ Learn about

When answering subtraction problems, it always helps to know the different ways subtraction problems can be worded.

minus   take away   decrease   subtract   find the difference

less than

a) What is 76 take away 37? ....

b) What is the difference between 93 and 32? ....

c) How many less than 49 is 17? ....

d) Decrease 84 by 45. ....

▼ Now try these

A squirrel collected 123 nuts ready to eat during the winter months.

a. During the first month he ate 34. He had .... nuts left.

b. During the second month he ate 36. He had .... nuts left.

c. During the third month he ate 35. He had .... nuts left.

d. Do you think he felt hungry after the fourth month? ....

9

Counting in steps

▼ Warm up

a) Count on in 3s.

b) Count on in 4s.

▼ Learn about

It is important to be able to count on or count back in numbers.
It is much quicker if you can do this in steps. Fill in the missing numbers.

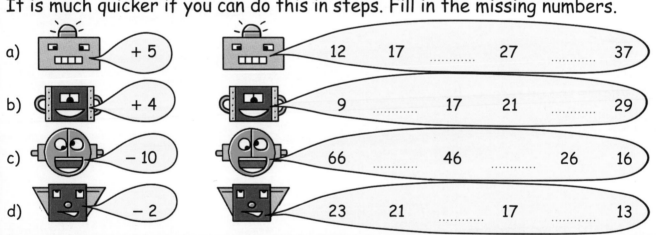

a) + 5   12   17   27   37

b) + 4   9   17   21   29

c) − 10   66   46   26   16

d) − 2   23   21   17   13

▼ Now try these

Write the rule in the machine and finish the sequence.

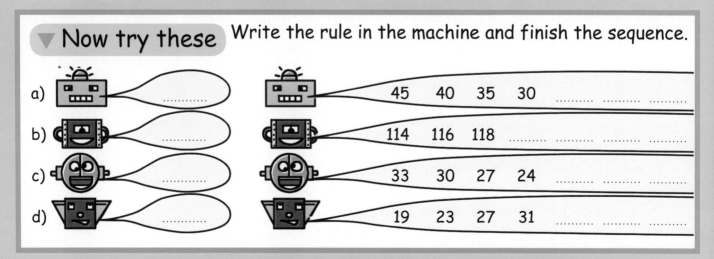

a)   45   40   35   30   ....

b)   114   116   118   ....

c)   33   30   27   24   ....

d)   19   23   27   31   ....

Counting in steps

▼ Warm up

Fill in the missing numbers.

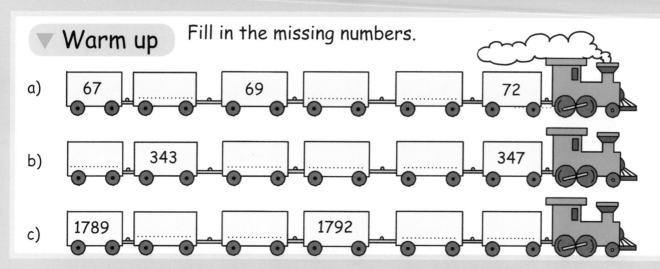

a) 67 ____ ____ 69 ____ ____ ____ 72

b) ____ 343 ____ ____ ____ ____ 347

c) 1789 ____ ____ 1792 ____ ____

▼ Learn about

First you need to find the **rule** when counting in steps.
Look carefully at these number lines.
Write the rules.

a) 342   340   338   336   334

rule = _____

b) 991   994   997   1000   1003

rule = _____

c) 122   126   130   134   138

rule = _____

d) 40   36   32   28   24

rule = _____

▼ Now try these

Fill in the missing numbers.
Remember to find the rule first!

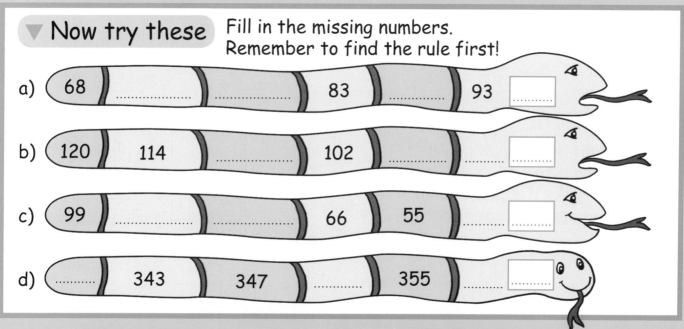

a) 68   ____   ____   83   ____   93   ____

b) 120   114   ____   102   ____   ____   ____

c) 99   ____   ____   66   55   ____   ____

d) ____   343   347   ____   355   ____

Numbers ending with 0

▼ Warm up
Add 10 to each of these numbers.

a) 67 ....

b) 340 ....

c) 123 ....

d) 456 ....

▼ Learn about
Once you know the value of each digit in a number, adding or subtracting multiples of 10, or 100, is easy.

Th	H	T	U
1	3	**4**	6

1346 + 30 = 1376 (3 tens are added to the tens column)

Th	**H**	T	U
1	**3**	4	6

1346 − 200 = 1146 (2 hundreds are subtracted from the hundreds column)

▼ Now try these
1. With a line, match the problems with their answers. The first one has been done for you.

230 − 20

135 + 50

44 + 70

110 − 60

175 − 80

400 + 300

50

95

185

700

114

210

2. George is doing a science experiment. How much liquid does he need to add to each bottle to make it equal 500ml? Write the answer under the test tube.

450ml

320ml

180ml

a) ....

b) ....

c) ....

Numbers ending with 0

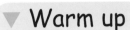

▼ Warm up

What is . . .

a) 500 + 700 = ...

b) 1400 − 500 = ...

c) 490 + 500 = ...

d) 1250 − 400 = ...

▼ Learn about

When finding what to add **to make 100**, round the units up first and then the tens.

24 + ? = 100

units first... 24 + 6 = 30
then tens... 30 + 70 = 100
76

24 + 76 = 100

▼ Now try these

1. Look at these children's test results.
How many more does each child have to get to make 100?

a) $\frac{74}{100}$ ....

b) $\frac{83}{100}$ ....

c) $\frac{27}{100}$ ....

d) $\frac{58}{100}$ ....

e) $\frac{64}{100}$ ....

2. Complete these number sentences.

a) 321 + ... = 400

b) 185 + ... = 200

c) 567 + ... = 600

d) 672 + ... = 700

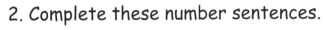

Multiplication facts

▼ Warm up

If 6 + 6 + 6 = 3 × 6, what is . . .

a) 5 + 5 + 5 + 5 + 5 = ...

b) 7 + 7 + 7 + 7 = ...

c) 4 + 4 + 4 + 4 + 4 + 4 = ...

▼ Learn about

Learning your **times tables** is very important. It will help you
with many other number problems without you even realizing it!
Watch out, multiplication problems can be worded in different ways.

multiply   times   find the product of . . .   multiplied by

1. What is 5 multiplied by 7?   ....

2. Double 6.   ....

3. Find the product of 3 and 9.   ....

4. Multiply 10 with 4.   ....

5. What are six sevens?   ....

6. What is 2 times 9?   ....

▼ Now try these

Answer these problems as quickly as possible.

a) 2 × 10 =.............   b) 3 × 5 = ...   c) 4 × 8 = ...   d) 5 × 8 =.............

e) 6 × 5 = ...   f) 4 × 4 = ...   g) 9 × 10 =.............   h) 3 = 7 =.............

i) 2 × 6 = ...   j) 10 × 5 = ...   k) 3 × 2 = ...   l) 8 × 3 = ...

14

Multiplication facts

▼ **Warm up** Times each of these numbers by 4.

a) ....

b) ....

c) ....

d) ....

e) ....

▼ **Learn about**

Complete this table. It will show the multiplication facts of the **6, 7, 8** and **9 times tables**.

×	1	2	3	4	5	6	7	8	9	10
6						36				
7		14								
8				32						
9									81	

▼ **Now try these**

1. Write a multiplication fact for each answer.
The first one has been done for you.

a) 5 × 9 = 45 b) .... = 12 c) .... = 63 d) .... = 90 e) .... = 9 f) .... = 49

2. Fill in the gaps as quickly as possible.

a) 6 × 4 = ...   b) 7 × .... = 21   c) .... × 6 = 54   d) 5 × .... = 40

e) 6 × .... = 36   f) 8 × 3 = ...   g) .... × 4 = 24   h) 9 × 8 = ...

i) 9 × .... = 27   j) .... × 8 = 16   k) 6 × 9 = ...   l) 7 × .... = 28

10 and 100

▼ Warm up

Write the numbers that come out of the spaceships.

a) 6 ×10 = ...

b) 8 ×10 = ...

c) 5 ×10 = ...

d) 9 ×10 = ...

▼ Learn about

When a number is multiplied by 10 it becomes 10 times bigger.

2 multiplied by 10 = 20   The number 2 moves one place to the left.

If a number is multiplied by 100 it becomes 100 times bigger.

2 multiplied by 100 = 200   It moves two places to the left.

▼ Now try these

Put these numbers through these spaceships.

a) 34 ×10 = ...

b) 29 ×100 = ...

c) 21 ×10 = ...

d) 17 ×100 = ...

e) 138 ×10 = ...

f) 87 ×100 = ...

g) 296 ×10 = ...

h) 55 ×100 = ...

i) 79 ×10 = ...

j) 9 ×100 = ...

k) 876 ×10 = ...

l) 71 ×100 = ...

16

10 and 100

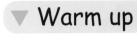
Write the numbers that come out of the spaceships.

a) 80 ÷10 ⚪ = ...

b) 30 ÷10 ⚪ = ...

c) 10 ÷10 ⚪ = ...

d) 70 ÷10 ⚪ = ...

▼ Learn about

When a number is divided by 10 it becomes 10 times smaller.

50 divided by 10 = 5   The number 5 moves one place to the right.

If a number is divided by 100 it becomes 100 times smaller.

500 divided by 100 = 5   It moves two places to the right.

▼ Now try these

1. Divide each of these numbers by 10, then 100.

	÷10	÷100
600		
2300		
7800		
9000		
800		

2. Fill in the stars to complete the number sentences.

a) 4400 ÷ ☆ = 44

b) 700 ÷ 100 = ☆

c) 500 ÷ ☆ ÷ 50

d) 7800 ÷ ☆ = 78

e) ☆ ÷ 10 = 1

f) ☆ ÷ 100 = 63

Doubles and halves

Double each of these numbers.

a) (10)......   b) (8)......   c) (5)......   d) (20)......   e) (6)......

▼ Learn about

If a number is doubled it is the same as multiplying the number by 2.

Fill in the answers.   double 16 = 16 × 2 = 32

a) double 15 ....   b) double 40 ....   c) double 26 ....   d) double 33 ....

▼ Now try these

1. With a line, match each number with its double.

The first one has been done for you.

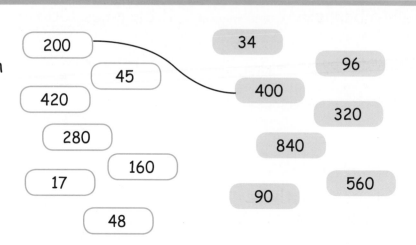

2. Najib swam two lengths of a 16 metre pool. How far did he swim? ....

3. On Saturday Emily earned £5.20 selling bookmarks. On Sunday Emily doubled her Saturday earnings. How much money did she make on Sunday? ....

4. Tim collected double the number of conkers as Sarah. Sarah collected 37. How many did Tim collect? ....

18

Doubles and halves

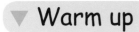

▼ **Warm up**

Halve each of these numbers.

a) 2 ⃝ ....   b) 10 ⃝ ....   c) 16 ⃝ ....   d) 8 ⃝ ....   e) 20 ⃝ ....

▼ **Learn about**

Halving does the opposite of doubling to a number.
If a number is halved, it is the same as dividing the number by 2.

$$\text{halve } 16 = 16 \div 2 = 8$$

a) halve 24 ....   b) halve 50 ....   c) halve 16 ....   d) halve 22 ....

▼ **Now try these**

1. Find half of each of the totals on the left. Circle the correct answer.
The first one has been done for you.

150	65	75	85	95
500	150	200	250	300
56	24	26	28	30
2400	1200	1250	1300	1350

2. This recipe makes 10 flapjacks. Daniel wants to make 5 flapjacks.
Rewrite the recipe for Daniel.

10 flapjacks need: **5 flapjacks need:**

120g of butter   .... of butter

48g of soft brown sugar   .... of soft brown sugar

6 tbsps of golden syrup   .... tbsps of golden syrup

300g of rolled oats   .... of rolled oats

19

Fractions

▼ Warm up   Colour the fraction on each circle.

a) $\frac{1}{2}$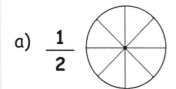

b) $\frac{3}{4}$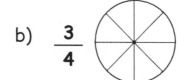

c) $\frac{1}{4}$

▼ Learn about   What do the numbers in a fraction mean?

top number = how many parts of the whole

bottom number = total number of parts that make a whole

$\frac{1}{4}$

▼ Now try these
1. If the shaded slices of cake are for me, how much of the cake is left for you?

a) 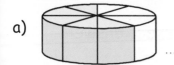 ....

b)  ....

c)  ....

d)  ....

e)  ....

f) 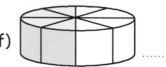 ....

2. Think of your favourite chocolate bar.
Circle the fraction you would prefer to eat.

$\frac{1}{2}$ $\frac{3}{4}$ $\frac{1}{3}$ $\frac{5}{8}$

Fractions

Write a different fraction for each pie.

a) ....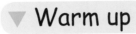

b) ....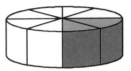

c) ....

▼ **Learn about**

'**Equivalent**' means 'having the same value'. Equivalent fractions have the same value. These are all equivalent fractions.

$\frac{1}{4}$

$\frac{2}{8}$

$\frac{3}{12}$

▼ **Now try these**

1. Write each of these equivalent fractions.

a) 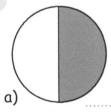 ....

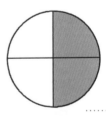 ....

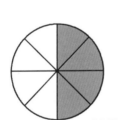 ....

b) 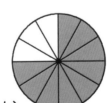 ....

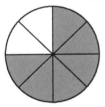 ....

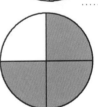 ....

2. How many would you have if you found the following:

a) $\frac{1}{2}$ of 10 sweets? ....

b) $\frac{1}{3}$ of 9 apples? ....

c) $\frac{1}{4}$ of 20 flowers? ....

21

Division facts

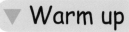

▼ Warm up

Divide each of these jars of sweets into two. How many sweets would each child get?

a)

b)

c)

....

▼ Learn about

When a number is **divided**, it is shared into equal groups.

$15 \div 3 = 5$ If 15 is shared into 3 equal groups there will be 5 in each group.

Division problems can be worded in different ways.

divide   share equally

▼ Now try these

Find the answers. Use the sweets to help.

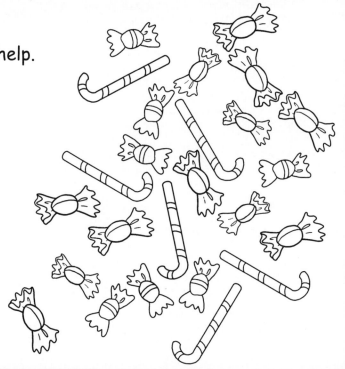

a) $10 \div 2 =$ ....

b) $16 \div 4 =$ ....

c) $20 \div 5 =$ ....

d) $12 \div 3 =$ ....

e) Divide 9 by 3. ....

f) Divide 25 by 5. ....

g) Share equally 15 into 5. ....

h) Share equally 18 into 3. ....

22

Division facts

▼ **Warm up**   Halve each of these numbers.

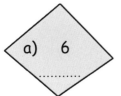 a) 6

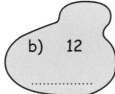 b) 12

 c) 40

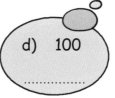 d) 100

e) 26

▼ **Learn about**

Your times tables can help with division facts. Look . . .

$3 \times 4 = 12$

$12 \div 3 = 4$

3 groups of 4 = 12

12 divided into 3 groups = 4

▼ **Now try these**

1. Use the multiplication fact to help you find the answers.

a) $2 \times 7 = 14$ $14 \div 2 =$ ....

b) $6 \times 3 = 18$ $18 \div 6 =$ ....

c) $5 \times 6 = 30$ $30 \div 6 =$ ....

d) $7 \times 4 = 28$ $28 \div 7 =$ ....

e) $3 \times 9 = 27$ $27 \div 9 =$ ....

f) $6 \times 6 = 36$ $36 \div 6 =$ ....

2. Sometimes a number can't be divided equally.
There are some remainders (r). Find the remainders.

a) $13 \div 2 = 6$ r ....

b) $16 \div 5 = 3$ r ....

c) $22 \div 4 = 5$ r ....

d) $18 \div 4 = 4$ r ....

Multiplying by 11 and 9

Multiply by 10.

a) 7 .... b) 24 .... c) 421 .... d) 690 .... e) 399 ....

▼ Learn about

Believe it or not, multiplying any number by 11 is easy!
Look . . .

First you multiply 27 by 10, and then you add one more 27.

$$27 \times 11 = (27 \times 10) + 27$$
$$= 270 + 27$$
$$= 297$$

▼ Now try these

Fill in the gaps with the correct information.

a) $32 \times 11 = ($ .... $\times 10) +$ ....

$= 320 + 32$

$=$ ....

b) $18 \times 11 = (18 \times$ .... $) + 18$

$=$ .... $+ 18$

$=$ ....

c) $61 \times 11 = ($ .... $\times 10) +$ ....

$=$ .... $+ 61$

$=$ ....

d) $25 \times 11 = ($ .... $\times$ .... $) +$ ....

$=$ .... $+$ ....

$=$ ....

Now do these on your own!

e) $17 \times 11 =$ ....

f) $52 \times 11 =$ ....

Multiplying by 11 and 9

▼ Warm up Multiply by 10.

 a) 16 ....

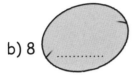 b) 8 ....

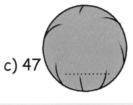 c) 47 ....

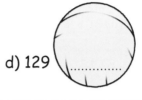 d) 129 ....

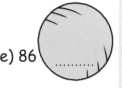 e) 86 ....

▼ Learn about

Multiplying any number by 9 is just as easy.

First you multiply 15 by 10, but this time you subtract 15.

$$15 \times 9 = (15 \times 10) - 15$$
$$= 150 - 15$$
$$= 135$$

▼ Now try these

Fill in the gaps with the correct information.

a) $22 \times 9 = ($ .... $\times 10) -$ ....

        $= 220 - 22$

        $=$ ....

b) $34 \times 9 = (34 \times$ .... $) - 34$

        $=$ .... $- 34$

        $=$ ....

c) $43 \times 9 = ($ .... $\times 10) -$ ....

        $=$ .... $- 43$

        $=$ ....

d) $55 \times 9 = ($ .... $\times$ .... $) -$ ....

        $=$ .... $-$ ....

        $=$ ....

Now do these on your own!

e) $19 \times 9 =$ ....

f) $24 \times 9 =$ ....

Checking calculations

▼ Warm up

Multiply these numbers by 10.

a) 45 .... b) 18 .... c) 27 .... d) 123 ....

▼ Learn about

Checking calculations is important.
Calculations can be checked in different ways.

Rounding gives an approximate answer.
19 + 42 is approximately the same as 20 + 40 = 60

So, you know the correct answer will be about 60. (It is actually 61.)

▼ Now try these

1. Round these numbers to the nearest 10.

a) 56 .... b) 72 .... c) 891 .... d) 44 .... e) 237 .... f) 99 ....

2. Look at the sum on the left. Circle the best approximation for it from those on the right. The first one has been done for you.

a)	57 + 39	50 + 40	⬭60 + 40⬭ 60 + 30
b)	177 − 34	180 − 30	180 − 40 170 − 30
c)	55 × 21	50 × 20	60 × 20 50 × 30
d)	96 ÷ 11	90 ÷ 10	90 ÷ 20 100 ÷ 10

3. Find an approximate answer.

a) 256 + 69 = ... b) 78 − 22 = ...

26

Checking calculations

a) 180 + 40 = ...   b) 335 + 20 = ...   c) 290 + 55 = ...

▼ Learn about

Inverse operations are another way of checking calculations.
Inverse means the 'opposite'.

Remember, division problems can be solved using multiplication (see page 23).

$$55 \div 11 = 5 \qquad 5 \times 11 = 55$$

Addition and subtraction problems can also help each other (see page 5).

$$230 + 45 = 275 \qquad 275 - 230 = 45$$

▼ Now try these

1. Write the inverse operation of each of these number sentences.
The first one has been done for you.

a) $54 \div 9 = 6$ ....9.... × ....6.... = ..54..

b) $18 \times 45 = 810$ .... ÷ .... = ...

c) $56 - 19 = 37$ .... + ... = ...

d) $78 + 23 = 101$ .... − .... = ...

e) $110 \div 22 = 5$ .... × .... = ...

f) $348 - 213 = 135$ .... + ... = ...

2. Using the numbers 6, 8 and 48 write four different
multiplication and division number sentences.

1. ....   2. ....

3. ....   4. ....

27

Number hunt

▼ Warm up

a) 17 + ... = 20   b) 20 − .... = 13   c) 14 + ... = 20   d) 20 − .... = 9

▼ Learn about

In a mental maths test it is important to answer questions quickly and accurately. How quickly can you answer the questions below? Write your answers in pencil and time yourself.

If you want to challenge yourself again you can rub out the answers and try to beat your time in a couple of days!

▼ Now try these

1) 23 + 23 = ...   2) 7 × 5 = ...   3) 25 − 9 = ...   4) 45 ÷ 9 = ...

5) 6 × 4 = ...   6) 41 − 8 = ...   7) 50 ÷ 5 = ...   8) 72 + 7 = ...

9) 8 × 3 = ...   10) 36 ÷ 4 = ...   11) 27 − 9 = ...   12) 6 × 6 = ...

13) 17 + 27 = ...   14) 7 × 4 = ...   15) 14 ÷ 7 = ...   16) 35 ÷ 7 = ...

17) 61 + 15 = ...   18) 44 − 6 = ...   19) 36 − 17 = ...   20) 8 × 6 = ...

21) 42 − 12 = ...   22) 10 ÷ 5 = ...   23) 6 × 9 = ...   24) 16 + 4 = ...

25) 9 × 10 = ...   26) 24 ÷ 8 = ...   27) 33 + 33 = ...   28) 16 − 8 = ...

29) 50 ÷ 5 = ...   30) 15 + 23 = ...   31) 7 × 7 = ...   32) 120 − 70 = ...

Number hunt

▼ **Warm up**

a) total 45 and 55 ....

b) increase 7 by 14 ....

c) double 36 ....

▼ Learn about

You often need to be careful when tackling maths problems that are written in words.

- Always read the problems through more than once so you are sure what, exactly, the question is asking.
- Work through the problems one step at a time.

▼ Now try these

You may need to do your workings on a separate piece of paper.

1. Jess read 38 pages of her book.
That night she read a further 24.
How many pages had she read altogether? ....

The book had a total of 100 pages.
How many more pages does Jess have to read to finish the book? ....

2. Tuhil was given £10.00 as a birthday present.
He decided to buy a number of small model cars to add to his collection.
He bought 9 cars, each costing 25p. How much did the cars cost him? ....

How much change did he get? ....

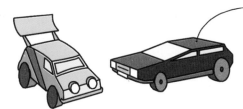

3. Tom was brilliant at cricket. In the first match
of the season he scored 25 runs, the second 32
and the third 22. In the first two matches how many runs did he score? ....

In the third and fourth matches he scored the same number of runs.
In all four matches how many runs did he score in total? ....

Answers

Page 4
WU
a) 11   b) 19   c) 14   d) 17
e) 14   f) 18   g) 17   h) 19

LA
a) 8   b) 16   c) 3   d) 7
e) 15   f) 2

NTT
1.
a) 7, 13   b) 6, 14   c) 9, 11   d) 8, 12
2. £20
3. 20 balloons

Page 5
WU
a) 3   b) 8   c) 8   d) 7   e) 3
f) 13   g) 9   h) 2

LA
a) correct b) incorrect c) correct

NTT
1. a) 17 b) 3 c) 0 d) 20 e) 13 f) 7
2. 13 friends
3. 7 packets

Page 6
WU
a) £1.52   b) 70p   c) £1.10
d) £1.60   e) £1.40   f) £3.00

NTT
1. a) 85 b) 49 c) 67 d) 67 e) 99

Page 7
WU
a) 45   b) 103 c) 87 d) 69 e) 51

LA
1. 36
2. 44
3. 89
4. 45

NTT
1. 71 skips
2. 86 skips

Page 8
WU
a) 23   b) 5   c) 11   d) 30   e) 9

NTT
1. e.g.
a) 49-32=17 b) 56-39=17
c) 49-17=32 d) 56-49=7 e) 56-32=24
2. a) 9cm b) 14cm c) 18cm

Page 9
WU
a) 19   b) 22   c) 49   d) 19
e) 19   f) 69

LA
a) 39   b) 61   c) 32   d) 39

NTT
a. 89 nuts   b. 53 nuts   c. 18 nuts
d. yes (only 18 nuts left for final month)

Page 10
WU
a) 6, 9, 12, 15, 18, 21
b) 10, 14, 18, 22, 26, 30

LA
a) 22, 32
b) 13, 25
c) 56, 36
d) 19, 15

NTT
a) Rule = -5 25, 20, 15
b) Rule = +2 120, 122, 124, 126
c) Rule = -3 21, 18, 15
d) Rule = +4 35, 39, 43

Page 11
WU
a) 67, 68, 69, 70, 71, 72
b) 342, 343, 344, 345, 346, 347
c) 1789, 1790, 1791, 1792, 1793, 1794

LA
a) Rule = -2
b) Rule = +3
c) Rule = +4
d) Rule = -4

NTT
a) 73, 78, 88 Rule = +5
b) 108, 96, 90 Rule = -6
c) 88, 77, 44 Rule = -11
d) 339, 351, 359 Rule = +4

Page 12
WU
a) 77 b) 350 c) 133 d) 466

NTT
1.
135 + 50 = 185
230 - 20 = 210
44 + 70 = 114
110 - 60 = 50
175 - 80 = 95
400 + 300 = 700
2.
a) 50ml b) 180ml c) 320ml

Page 13
WU
a) 1200 b) 900 c) 990 d) 850

NTT
a) 26 b) 17 c) 73 d) 42 e) 36
a) 79 b) 15 c) 33 d) 28

Page 14
WU
a) 5 x 5 b) 4 x 7 c) 6 x 4

LA
1. 35
2. 12
3. 27
4. 40
5. 42
6. 18

NTT
a) 20   b) 15   c) 32   d) 40   e) 30
f) 16   g) 90   h) 21   i) 12   j) 50
k) 6   l) 24

Page 15
WU
a) 20 b) 32 c) 8 d) 28 e) 36

Answers

LA

×	1	2	3	4	5	6	7	8	9	10
6	6	12	18	24	30	36	42	48	54	60
7	7	14	21	28	35	42	49	56	63	70
8	8	16	24	32	40	48	56	64	72	80
9	9	18	27	36	45	54	63	72	81	90

NTT

1.
a) 5 x 9 or 9 x 5
b) 2 x 6, 6 x 2, 3 x 4 or 4 x 3
c) 7 x 9 or 9 x 7
d) 10 x 9 or 9 x 10
d) 3 x 3
f) 7 x 7

2.
a) 24   b) 3   c) 9   d) 8   e) 6   f) 24
g) 6   h) 72   i) 3   j) 2   k) 54   l) 4

Page 16
WU
a) 60   b) 80   c) 50   d) 90

NTT
a) 340   b) 2900   c) 210   d) 1700
e) 1380   f) 8700   g) 2960   h) 5500
i) 790   j) 900   k) 8760   l) 7100

Page 17
WU
a) 8   b) 3   c) 1   d) 7

NTT
1.

	÷ 10	÷ 100
600	60	6
2300	230	23
7800	780	78
9000	900	90
800	80	8

2.
a) 100   b) 7   c) 10
d) 100   e) 10   f) 6300

Page 18
WU
a) 20   b) 16   c) 10   d) 40   e) 12

LA
a) 30   b) 80   c) 52   d) 66

NTT
1.
200 = 400
45 = 90
420 = 840
280 = 560
160 = 320
17 = 34
48 = 96
32 metres
£10.40
74 conkers

Page 19
WU
1, 5, 8, 4, 10

LA
12, 25, 8, 11

NTT
150 = 75
500 = 250
56 = 28
2400 = 1200
2.
60g of butter
24g of brown sugar
3 tbsps of golden syrup
150g of rolled oats

Page 20
WU
a)

b)

c)

NTT

1. a) $\frac{3}{8}$ b) $\frac{3}{4}$ c) $\frac{5}{6}$
   d) $\frac{1}{2}$ e) $\frac{7}{12}$ f) $\frac{4}{8}$
2. $\frac{3}{4}$ is the largest fraction of chocolate!

Page 21
WU
a) $\frac{1}{4}$
b) $\frac{2}{8}$
c) $\frac{3}{12}$

NTT
1.
a) $\frac{1}{2}$, $\frac{2}{4}$, $\frac{4}{8}$
b) $\frac{9}{12}$, $\frac{6}{8}$, $\frac{3}{4}$
2.
a) 5 sweets
b) 3 apples
c) 5 flowers

Answers

Page 22

WU

a) 5 b) 8 c) 10

NTT

a) 5 b) 4 c) 4 d) 4 e) 3 f) 5 g) 3 h) 6

Page 23

WU

a) 3 b) 6 c) 20 d) 50 e) 13

NTT

1. a) 7 b) 3 c) 5 d) 4 e) 3 f) 6
2. a) r1 b) r1 c) r2 d) r2

Page 24

WU

a) 70   b) 240   c) 4210
d) 6900 e) 3990

NTT

a) 32 x 11   = (32 x 10) + 32
              = 320 + 32
              = 352

b) 18 x 11   = (18 x 10) +18
              = 180 +18
              = 198

c) 61 x 11   = (61 x 10) + 61
              = 610 + 61
              = 671

d) 25 x 11   = (25 x 10) + 25
              = 250 + 25
              = 275

e) 17 x 11   = (17 x 10) + 17
              = 170 + 17
              = 187

f) 52 x 11   = (52 x 10) + 52
              = 520 + 52
              = 572

Page 25

WU

a) 160 b) 80 c) 470 d) 1290 e) 860

NTT

a) 22 x 9   = (22 x 10) - 22
              = 220 - 22
              = 198

b) 34 x 9   = (34 x 10) - 34
              = 340 - 34
              = 306

c) 43 x 9   = (43 x 10) - 43
              = 430 - 43
              = 387

d) 55 x 9   = (55 x 10) - 55
              = 550 - 55
              = 495

e) 19 x 9   = (19 x 10) - 19
              = 190 - 19
              = 171

f) 24 x 9   = (24 x 10) - 24
              = 240 - 24
              = 216

Page 26

WU

a) 450 b) 180 d) 270 e) 1230

NTT

1.
a) 60 b) 70 c) 890 d) 40
e) 240 f) 100
2.
a) 60 + 40
b) 180 - 30
c) 60 x 20
d) 100 ÷ 10
3.
a) 330 b) 60

Page 27

WU

a) 220   b) 355   c) 345

NTT

1.
b) 810 ÷ 45 = 18 or 810 ÷ 18 = 45
c) 37 + 19 = 56 or 19 + 37 = 56
d) 101 – 78 = 23 or 101 – 23 = 78
e) 22 x 5 = 110 or 5 x 22 = 110
f) 213 + 135 = 348 or
   135 + 213 = 348
2. *e. g.*
1. 6 x 8 = 48
2. 8 x 6 = 48
3. 48 ÷ 6 = 8
4. 48 ÷ 8 = 6

Page 28

WU

a) 3   b) 7   c) 6   d) 11

NTT

1. 46   2. 35   3. 16   4. 5
5. 24   6. 33   7. 10   8. 79
9. 24   10. 9   11. 18   12. 36
13. 44   14. 28   15. 2   16. 5
17. 76   18. 38   19. 19   20. 48
21. 30   22. 2   23. 54   24. 20
25. 90   26. 3   27. 66   28. 8
29. 10   30. 38   31. 49   32. 50

Page 29

WU

a) 100 b) 21 c) 72

NTT

1. Jess – 62 pages, 38 pages
2. Tuhil – £2.25, £7.75
3. Tom – 57 runs, 101 runs